PENGUIN BO

WORTHLESS PL

Patrick Wright was born in 1945 in Abersoch, North Wales. He was educated at Barrow Hills Prep School and St George's College, Weybridge. He began his career as an illustrator of children's comics and went on to produce *Modesty Blaise* for the *Evening Standard* for a year. He switched to humorous cartooning in 1981 with the publication of his first book, *Walkies*, which was followed by five more books of cartoons. He has also worked extensively in all aspects of advertising.

Patrick Wright is married with two children and lives in West Sussex. His interests include his dog, rock and boogie piano playing, fine-scale model making, the films of Fassbinder, the Arts and Crafts movement and fifties American cars. He dislikes travel.

PATRICK WRIGHT

WORTHLESS PURSUITS

PENGUIN BOOKS

FOR NIGEL HOLLIS

PENGUIN BOOKS

Published by the Penguin Group
Penguin Books Ltd, 27 Wrights Lane, London W8 5TZ, England
Penguin Books USA Inc., 375 Hudson Street, New York, New York 10014, USA
Penguin Books Australia Ltd, Ringwood, Victoria, Australia
Penguin Books Canada Ltd, 10 Alcorn Avenue, Toronto, Ontario, Canada M4V 3B2
Penguin Books (NZ) Ltd, 182–190 Wairau Road, Auckland 10, New Zealand

Penguin Books Ltd, Registered Offices: Harmondsworth, Middlesex, England

First published 1992
1 3 5 7 9 10 8 6 4 2

Printed in England by Clays Ltd, St Ives plc

WORTHLESS PURSUITS No 1
ATTEMPTING TO TETHER YOUR ZEPPELIN TO THE SPIRE OF SALISBURY CATHEDRAL.

WORTHLESS PURSUITS No. 2
OFFERING THE LION A DOG BISCUIT.

WORTHLESS PURSUITS No 3
THROWING STONES AT GIANT LINERS.

WORTHLESS PURSUITS No.4
COUNTING THE SPOTS ON OTHER PEOPLE'S DALMATIANS.

WORTHLESS PURSUITS No 5
MAKING MOUNTAINS OUT OF MOLEHILLS.

WORTHLESS PURSUITS No 6
TRAINING TORTOISES TO JUMP THROUGH HOOPS OF FIRE.
PATRICK WRIGHT.

WORTHLESS PURSUITS No 7
BREEDING GIANT SQUIDS FOR PLEASURE AND PROFIT.
Patrick Wright.

WORTHLESS PURSUITS No 8
TAKING THE SLOTH FOR A WALK (AND TRYING TO ENJOY IT).

WORTHLESS PURSUITS No 9
RACING GIANT SLOTHS.
JACK BLACK
TURF ACCOUNTANT

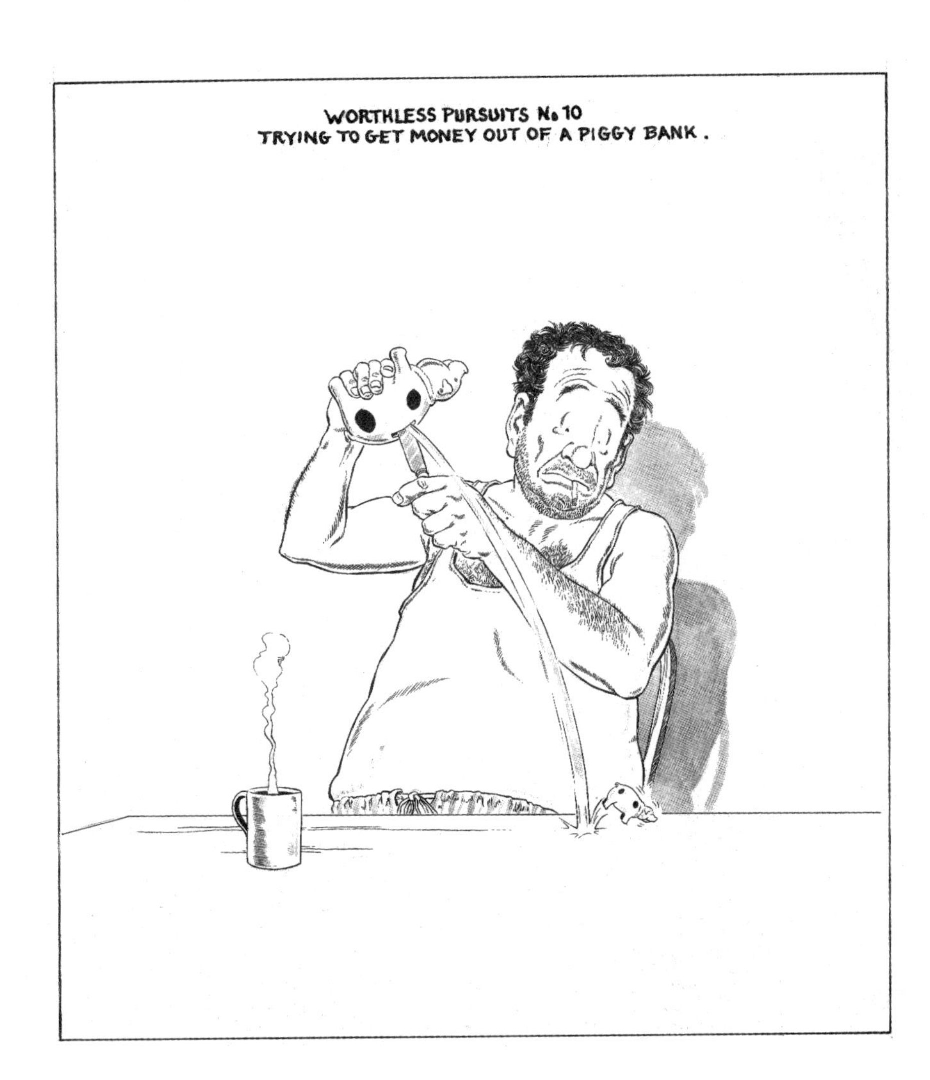
WORTHLESS PURSUITS No 10
TRYING TO GET MONEY OUT OF A PIGGY BANK.

WORTHLESS PURSUITS No 11
WORKING IN A PIGGY BANK.

WORTHLESS PURSUITS No 12
SMOKING FISH.

WORTHLESS PURSUITS No 13
FISHING.

WORTHLESS PURSUITS No 14
TRYING TO SELL A TALKING COCKATOO WHEN IT'S LEARNT THE COMPLETE WORKS OF ANDREW LLOYD-WEBBER.

WORTHLESS PURSUITS No15
OPENING ON SUNDAYS.
SALE
SUPERSTORE
SALE
SALE
SALE
WE ARE OPEN!
PATRICK WRIGHT

WORTHLESS PURSUITS No 16
WELCOMING THE BLACK SHEEP OF THE FAMILY BACK INTO THE FOLD.

WORTHLESS PURSUITS No 17
MOUNTING A PRODUCTION OF 'WAR AND PEACE' IN THE VILLAGE HALL.

WORTHLESS PURSUITS No 18
EXPECTING YOUR BANK MANAGER TO HELP YOU WITH YOUR PROBLEMS.
HE LISTENING BA

WORTHLESS PURSUITS No 19
SYNCHRONISED SWIMMING IN A FORCE TEN GALE.

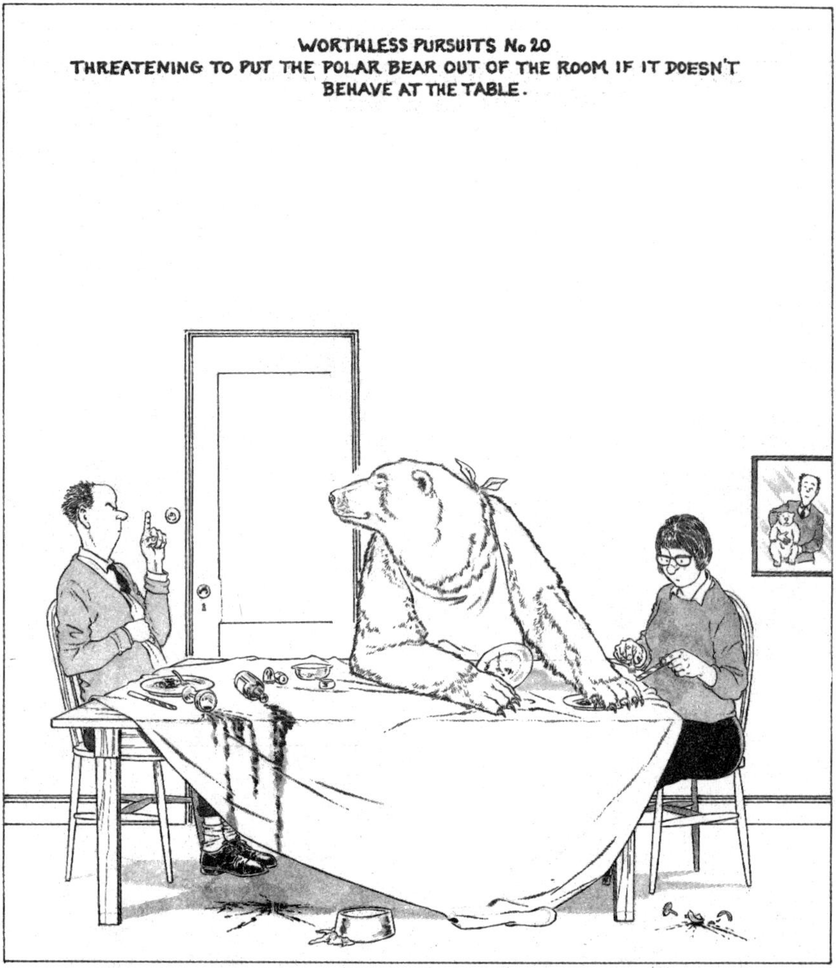

WORTHLESS PURSUITS No 20

THREATENING TO PUT THE POLAR BEAR OUT OF THE ROOM IF IT DOESN'T BEHAVE AT THE TABLE.

WORTHLESS PURSUITS No 21
VISITING OLD FRIENDS.
DEAR BRIAN,
SORRY ABOUT
THIS EVENING
BUT I'VE BEEN
CALLED AWAY
SUDDENLY.
LET'S GET
TOGETHER WH
I GET BACK.
ALL THE BEST
Bob.

WORTHLESS PURSUITS No. 22
USING A BLACK & DECKER CHAINSAW AT THE TOP OF A LADDER.
Patrick Wright.

WORTHLESS PURSUITS No.23
TRYING TO PICK YOUR NOSE WITHOUT BEING SEEN.

WORTHLESS PURSUITS No 24
PICKING OTHER PEOPLE'S NOSES.

WORTHLESS PURSUITS No 25
COMPLAINING TO THE WAITER THAT YOUR SOUP SPOON IS DIRTY.

WORTHLESS PURSUITS No26
PLAYING TEST CRICKET IN A RAIN FOREST.

WORTHLESS PURSUITS No 27
TRYING TO KILL TWO BIRDS WITH ONE STONE.
MOD V/EXP/91
POINT No 1
TARGET No 1.
POINT No 2.
TARGET No 2.
VELOCITY
TRAJECTORY

WORTHLESS PURSUITS No 28
COUNTING YOUR CHICKENS BEFORE THEY'VE HATCHED.

WORTHLESS PURSUITS No 29
EMPLOYING A GERMAN ABSTRACT EXPRESSIONIST TO PAINT YOUR DAUGHTER'S PORTRAIT.

WORTHLESS PURSUITS No 30
AGREEING TO LET THE ARTIST PAINT YOUR PORTRAIT IN THE DARK .

WORTHLESS PURSUITS No 31
LAUNCHING THE LIFEBOAT ON THE VILLAGE POND.

WORTHLESS PURSUITS No 32
CATCHING RHINOS WITH A BUTTERFLY NET.

WORTHLESS PURSUITS No 33
PAINTING BATTLESHIPS WITH WATER-COLOURS.

WORTHLESS PURSUITS No. 34
INVITING THE NEW NEIGHBOURS IN FOR A DRINK.

WORTHLESS PURSUITS No 35
TRYING TO STUDY PHILOSOPHY AT THE FAIRGROUND.
OTING GALLERY

WORTHLESS PURSUITS No 36
COMPETITION BALLROOM DANCING WITH MATTRESSES.

WORTHLESS PURSUITS No. 37
BEING A GOVERNMENT HEALTH INSPECTOR.

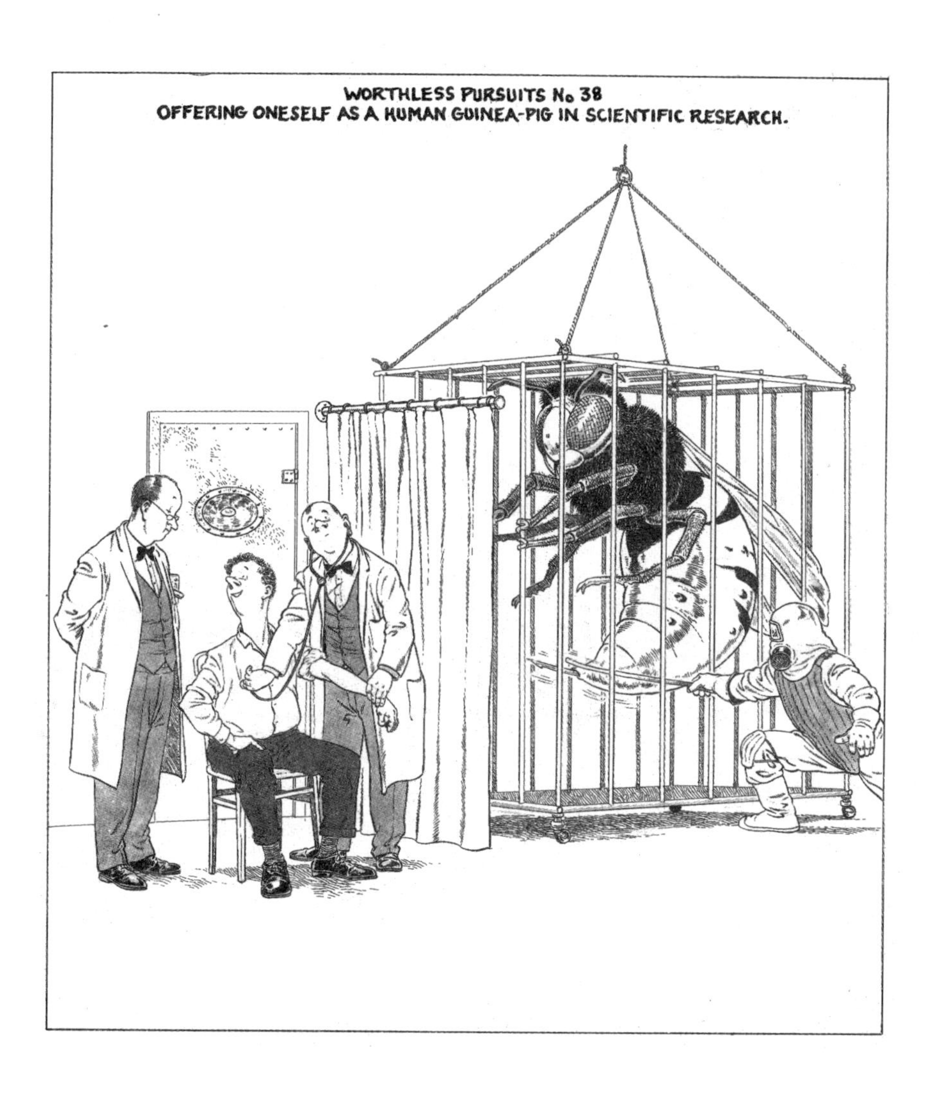
WORTHLESS PURSUITS No 38
OFFERING ONESELF AS A HUMAN GUINEA-PIG IN SCIENTIFIC RESEARCH.

WORTHLESS PURSUITS No. 39

BEING A SAMURAI ANYWHERE OTHER THAN JAPAN.

BUS STOP

WORTHLESS PURSUITS No 40
SERVING GOURMET MEALS FROM A MOBILE CAFE.
Les Alouettes
(MOBILE CAFE)
PROP: JEAN MARIE LARKIN
(& SONS)
Specialities
Velouté aux grenouilles.
Sole mon désir.
Calamars sauce Amoricaine.
Moules au cidre de Normandie
Escargots aux herbes.
MUTHA HUMPIN' TRUCKER
TODAY

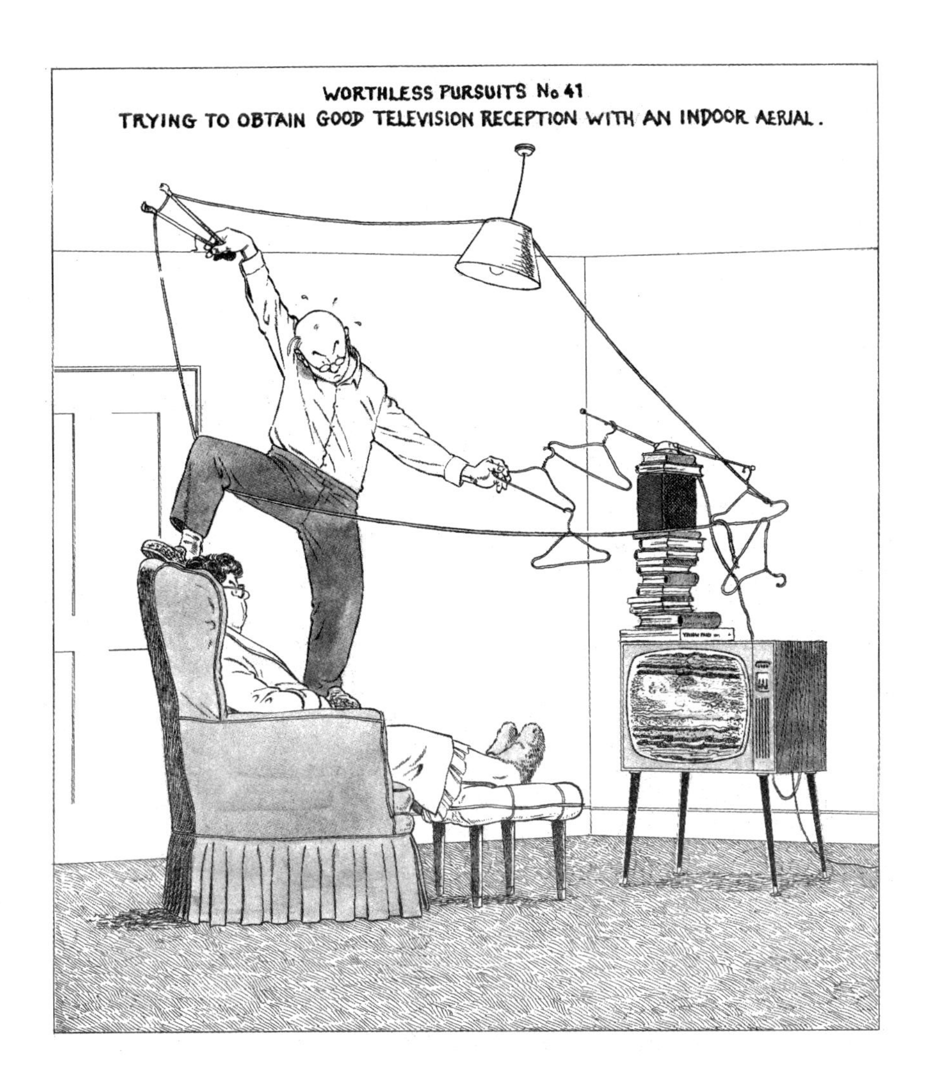
WORTHLESS PURSUITS No 41
TRYING TO OBTAIN GOOD TELEVISION RECEPTION WITH AN INDOOR AERIAL.

WORTHLESS PURSUITS No 42
COLLECTING SUPERMARKET TROLLEYS FROM TIBET.

WORTHLESS PURSUITS No 43
TRYING TO GET THROUGH THE 'EXPRESS CHECKOUT' WHEN THERE'S A PHILOSOPHER BEHIND THE TILL.

WORTHLESS PURSUITS No 44
BEING THE REAR END OF A PANTOMIME HORSE.

WORTHLESS PURSUITS No 45
VOLUNTEERING TO ASSIST MAGICIANS, (ESPECIALLY 'MARVO')
the Amazing
MARVO
the
MAD MAGICIAN
featuring
THE MOST DANGEROUS
ACT ON EARTH!
(for one night only)

WORTHLESS PURSUITS No 46
GILDING THE FALL-OUT SHELTER.

WORTHLESS PURSUITS No 47
FILLING A CONDOM WITH WATER FROM THE GARDEN STANDPIPE.
1889
St JOHN THOMAS SCHOOL
REPENT OR DIE!
BOMB DISPOSAL

WORTHLESS PURSUITS No 48
ATTENDING A BARBECUE IN A BLIZZARD.

WORTHLESS PURSUITS No 49
COLLECTING GREASE FROM BEARS.

WORTHLESS PURSUITS No 50
TRYING TO GET GIANT PANDAS TO MATE.
1 + 1 = 3
FANCIES YOU
PLAYBOY
IF YOU DON'T GET ON WITH IT YOU'LL BE EXTINCT

WORTHLESS PURSUITS No 51
TRYING TO IMPRESS YOUR NEIGHBOURS WITH
YOUR HUNTING TROPHIES .
ADOLF

WORTHLESS PURSUITS No 52
EXPECTING A DECENT SHAVE FROM A TALKATIVE BARBER.

WORTHLESS PURSUITS No.53
COLLECTING CUCKOO CLOCKS.

WORTHLESS PURSUITS No54
EXPERIMENTING WITH ANIMALS.
GROWTH ACCELERATOR

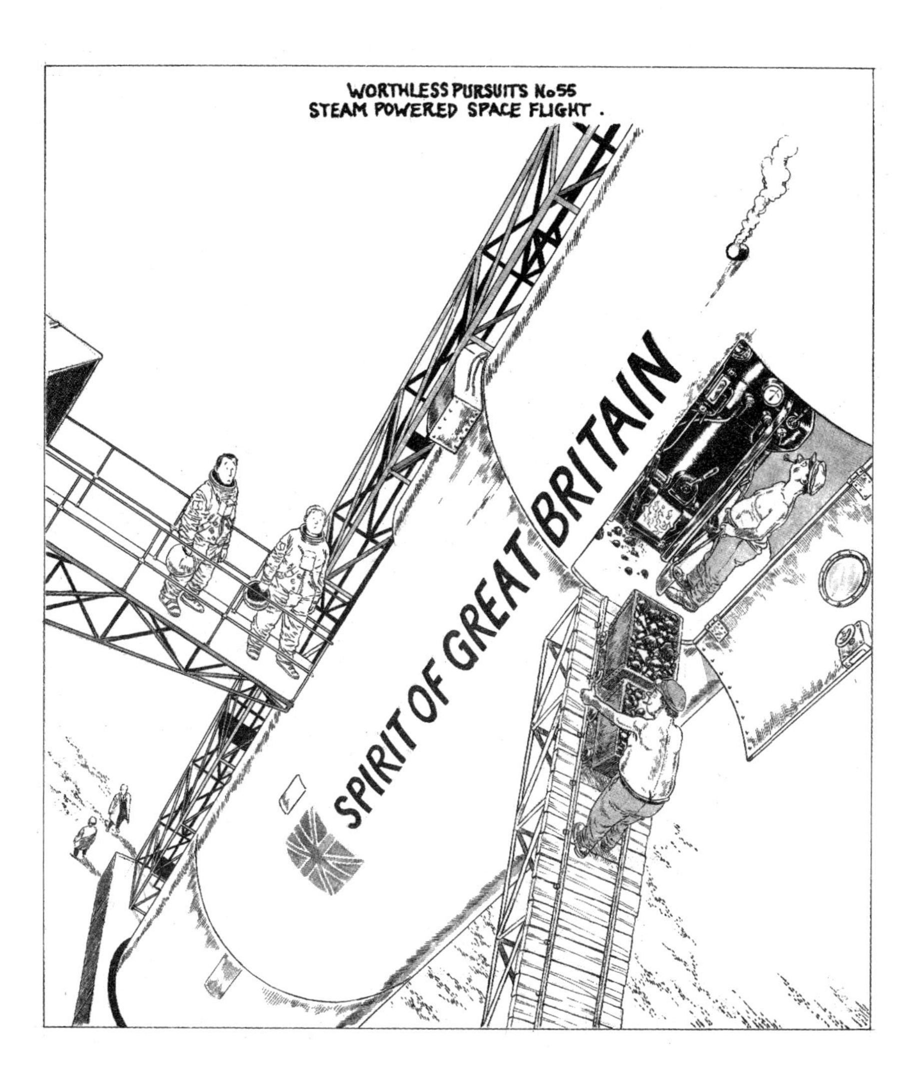
WORTHLESS PURSUITS No 55
STEAM POWERED SPACE FLIGHT.
SPIRIT OF GREAT BRITAIN

WORTHLESS PURSUITS No56
TRYING TO BURN YOURSELF TO DEATH IN PUBLIC.

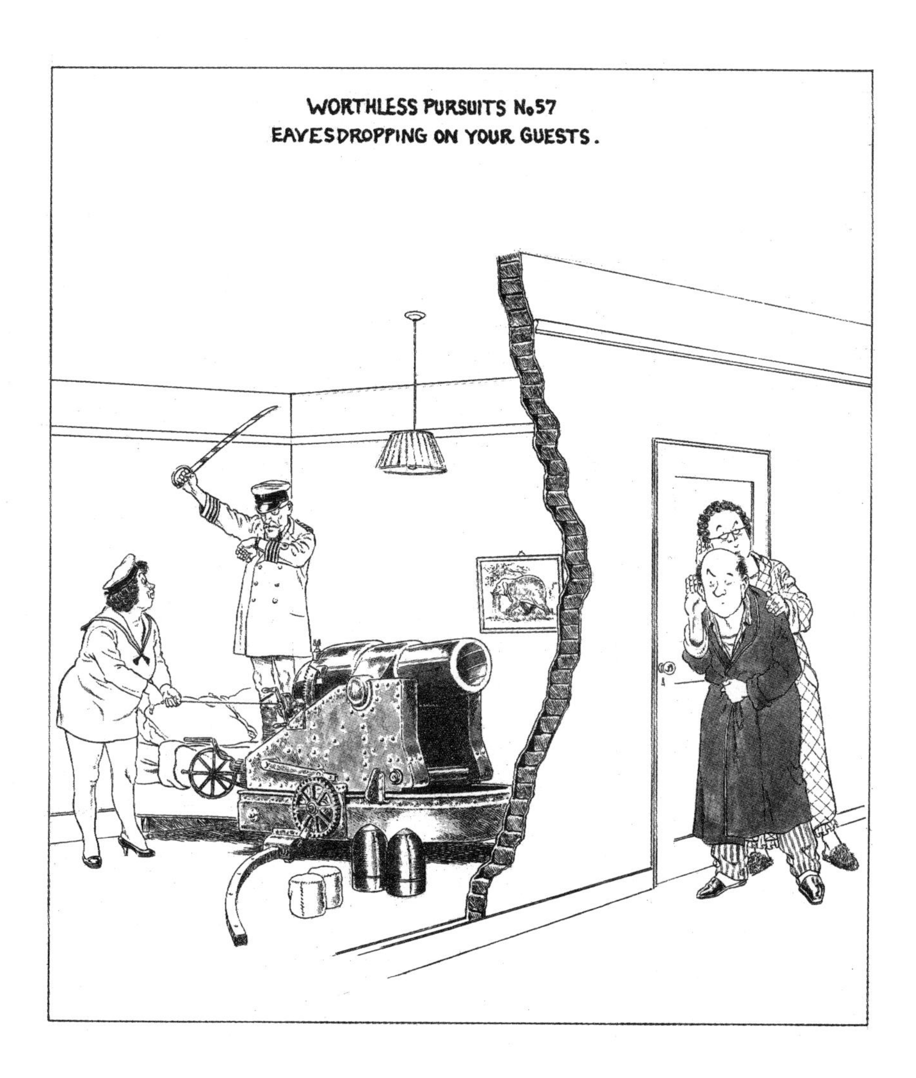
WORTHLESS PURSUITS No57
EAVESDROPPING ON YOUR GUESTS.

WORTHLESS PURSUITS No 58
GOING TO THE SOUTH POLE .
H.M.
INSPECTOR OF TAXES
Patrick Wright.

WORTHLESS PURSUITS No 59
CARRYING AN ALBATROSS AROUND YOUR NECK.

WORTHLESS PURSUITS No 60
BEING THE ONLY PLUMBER IN THE SAHARA.
FAST, FRIENDLY SERVICE!
F&M. FLOOD.
HIGH CLASS PLUMBERS
CENTRAL HEATING SPECIALISTS.
Est 1959
BATHROOM AND KITCHEN EXPERTS.
QUALITY WORK GUARANTEED!
SUPPLIERS OF
mira
Twyfords
SHIRES
ARMITAGE SHANKS
SHOWROOM
SALE NOW ON!
HUGE DISCOUNTS
F&M. FLOOD. SPECIALIST
TOILETS-TANKS-TAPS-
BOILERS-IMMERSION
BURST PIPES-SHOWERS-
24 HOUR SERVICE 365 DAYS A
NO CALL OUT CHARGE!
F&M

WORTHLESS PURSUITS No 61
MARCHING ARMIES OF ELEPHANTS ACROSS THE ALPS.

WORTHLESS PURSUITS No62
HOLDING A PARTY FOR CHILDREN.
10

WORTHLESS PURSUITS No63
TRYING TO RAISE THE TITANIC -
VENTURE III

WORTHLESS PURSUITS No 64
AGREEING TO LOOK AFTER THE NEIGHBOURS' CHRYSALIS WHILE THEY ARE AWAY.

WORTHLESS PURSUITS No 65

TRYING TO IMPRESS YOUR COLLEAGUE WITH THE NUMBER OF TINY OBJECTS YOU'VE MANAGED TO SQUEEZE INTO A MATCHBOX.

WORTHLESS PURSUITS No 66
TRYING TO DISCOVER WHO FARTED IN CHURCH.

WORTHLESS PURSUITS No 67

TRYING TO BE A SUCCESSFUL CRIMINAL WHEN YOU'VE GOT TWO HEADS.

WORTHLESS PURSUITS No. 68
BEING THE SUBJECT OF 'THIS IS YOUR LIFE'.

WORTHLESS PURSUITS No 69
BUYING AND TRYING TO SELL OLD MASTERS.

WORTHLESS PURSUITS No 70
BEING THE BOUNCER AT A PLAY GROUP.
KIDDIE WINKIES
PLAY GROUP
MON – FRI 9 O'CLOCK – 1 O'CLOCK
PLAYGROUP LEADER: MRS URSULA SNITE.

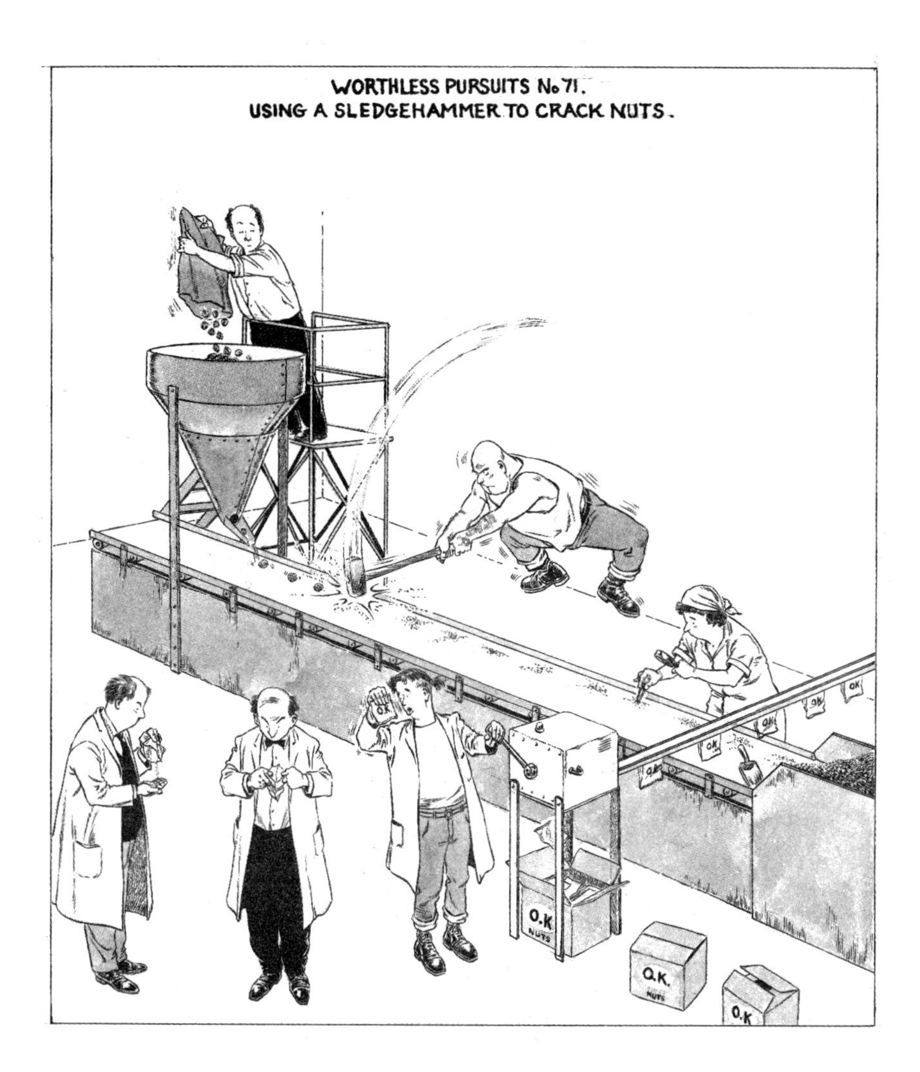
WORTHLESS PURSUITS No 71.
USING A SLEDGEHAMMER TO CRACK NUTS.
O.K
NUTS
O.K.
NUTS
O.K

WORTHLESS PURSUITS No 72
COMBING YOUR HAIR.

WORTHLESS PURSUITS No. 73
TRYING TO CONVINCE YOURSELF AND OTHERS THAT YOU'RE GETTING BETTER.

WORTHLESS PURSUITS No 74
TRYING TO DIRECT TRAFFIC WHEN YOU'VE FORGOTTEN TO PUT YOUR CLOTHES ON.

WORTHLESS PURSUITS No 75
WAITING TO BECOME A KING.